The Easy Key...

The Eighties
23 classic songs for keyboard

© International Music Publications Ltd

First published in 1995 by International Music Publications Ltd

International Music Publications Ltd is a Faber Music company

3 Queen Square, London WC1N 3AU

Music arranged and processed by Barnes Music Engraving Ltd

Cover image Deborah Roundtree / The Imagebank

Printed in England by Caligraving Ltd

All rights reserved

ISBN 0-571-52568-7

Anything For You

Words and Music by Gloria Estefan

Suggested Registration: Flute
Rhythm: Soft Rock
Tempo: ♩ = 69

A - ny - thing for you though you're not here,_ since you said we're through it

seems like years, time keeps drag-ging on and on, and for - ev - er's been and gone, still I can't

fig-ure what went wrong. ___ I'd still do a - ny-thing for you, I'll play your game, you

hurt me through and through,_ but you can have your way. ___ I can pre-

- tend each time I see you,_ that I don't care, and I don't need you,_ and though you'll

ne - ver see me cry - ing,_ you know in - side I feel like dy - ing, ___ and I'd do

Bad Boys

Words and Music by George Michael

Suggested Registration: Trumpet
Rhythm: 16 Beat
Tempo: ♩ = 120

Dear Mum - my, dear Dad-dy, you had plans for me, oh yeah,

__ I was your on - ly son, __ and long be - fore this ba - by boy could

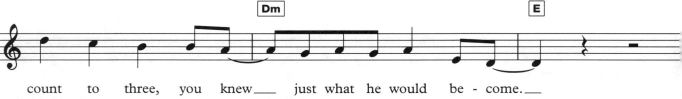

count to three, you knew __ just what he would be - come. __

Run a - long to school, no child of mine grows up a fool, __ run a - long to school.

When you tried to tell me what to do, __ I just

shut my mouth and smiled at you. One thing that I know for sure, __

Blue Eyes

Words by Gary Anthony Osborne / Music by Elton John

Suggested Registration: Harmonica
Rhythm: Slow Rock 6/8
Tempo: ♩ = 70

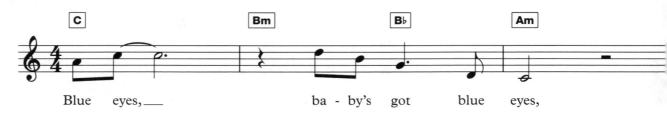

Blue eyes,___ ba-by's got blue eyes,

like a deep blue sea on a blue, blue

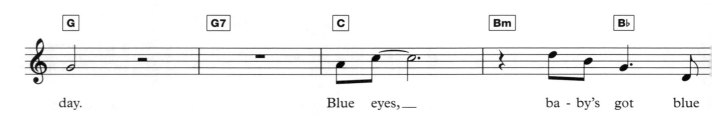

day. Blue eyes,___ ba-by's got blue

eyes, when the morn - ing comes,

I'll be far a - way, and I say,___

blue eyes hold - ing back the tears, hold - ing back the

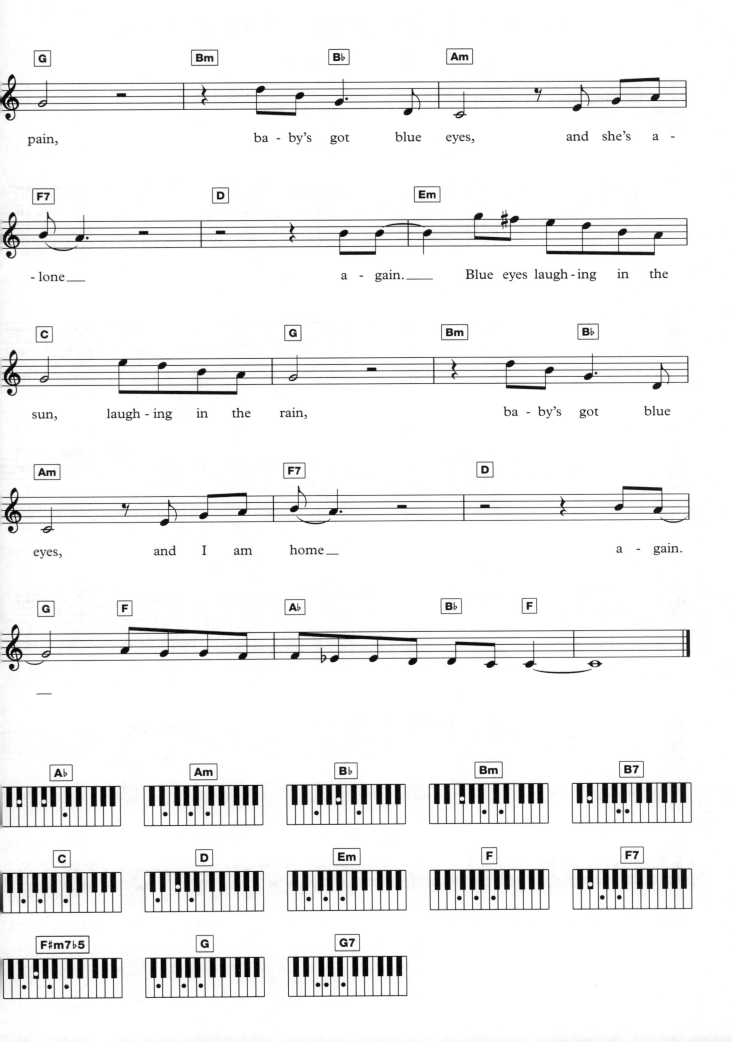

Can't Stay Away From You

Words and Music by Gloria Estefan

Suggested Registration: Electric Piano
Rhythm: Soft Rock
Tempo: ♩ = 80

Time flies when you're hav - ing fun, I heard some-bo - dy

say. But if all_ I've been is fun, then ba - by, let_ me

go, don't wan-na be in your way. And I don't wan-na be_ your

sec - ond choice, don't wan-na be just_ your friend.

You keep tell - ing me that_ you're not in love,_

you wan-na throw it all a - way. But I can't stay a-way from

CHINA IN YOUR HAND

Words and Music by Carol Decker and Ron Rogers

Suggested Registration: Vibraphone
Rhythm: Soft Rock
Tempo: ♩ = 124

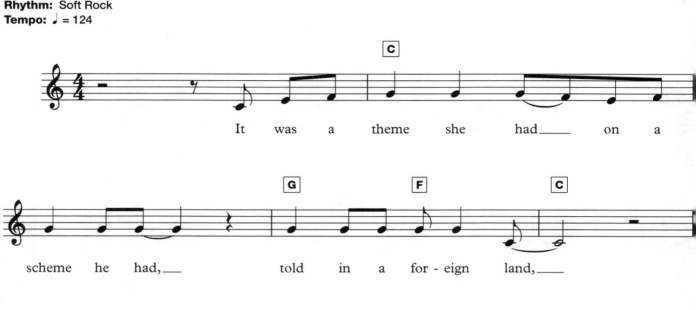

It was a theme she had____ on a scheme he had,____ told in a for-eign land,____

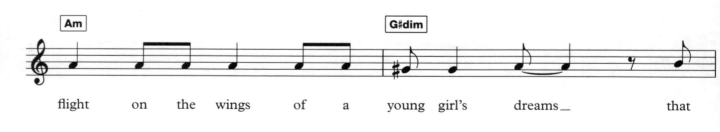

to take life on earth__ to the sec - ond birth,_ and the

man was in____ com - mand.____ It was a

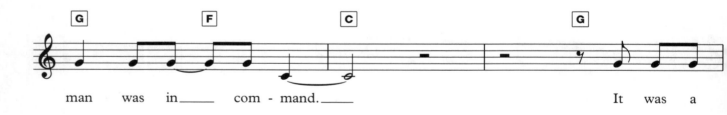

flight on the wings of a young girl's dreams__ that

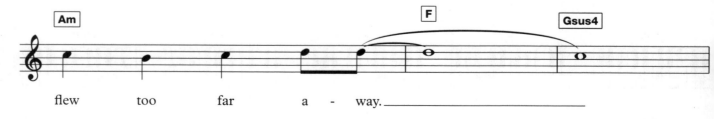

flew too far a - way.____

12

CLUB TROPICANA

Words and Music by George Michael and Andrew Ridgeley

Suggested Registration: Electric Piano
Rhythm: 16 Beat
Tempo: ♩ = 108

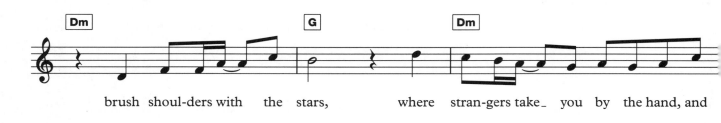

Let me take_ you to the place where mem-ber-ship's a smil-ing face,

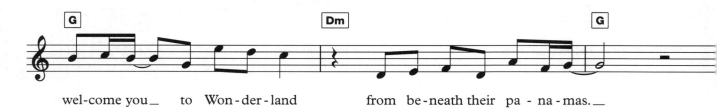

brush shoul-ders with the stars, where stran-gers take_ you by the hand, and

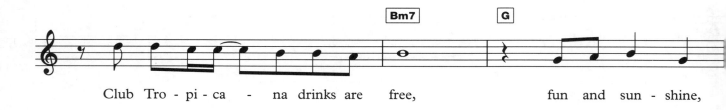

wel-come you_ to Won-der-land from be-neath their pa-na-mas._

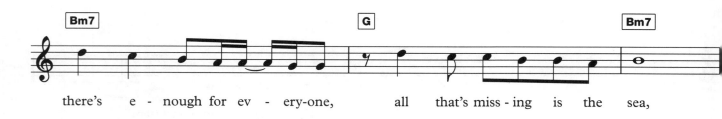

Club Tro-pi-ca - na drinks are free, fun and sun-shine,

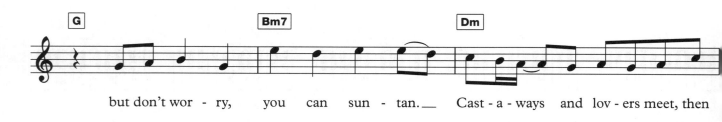

there's e-nough for ev-ery-one, all that's miss-ing is the sea,

but don't wor-ry, you can sun-tan._ Cast-a-ways and lov-ers meet, then

kiss in Tro - pi - ca - na's heat. Watch the waves break on the bay,

soft white sands, a blue la - goon, cock - tail time,_ a sum - mer's tune,

a whole night's ho - li - day._____ Club Tro - pi - ca - na drinks are

free, fun and sun - shine, there's e - nough for ev - ery-one,

all that's miss - ing is the sea, but don't wor - ry,

you can sun - tan. Club Tro - pi - ca - na._____

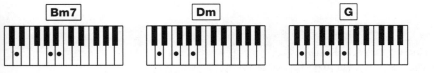

DON'T YOU WANT ME

Words and Music by Philip Oakey, Adrian Wright and Jo Callis

Suggested Registration: Synth Lead
Rhythm: 16 Beat
Tempo: ♩ = 120

You were work-ing as a wait-ress in a cock-tail bar

when I met you. I picked you out, I shook you up, and

turned you a - round, turned you in - to some-one new. Now

five years la - ter on you've got the world at your feet, suc -

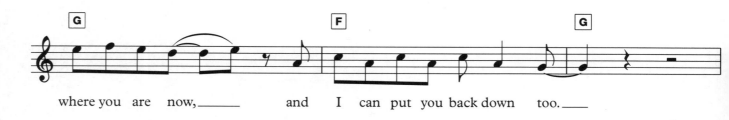

- cess has been so ea - sy for you, but don't for - get it's me who put you

where you are now, and I can put you back down too.

Everytime You Go Away

Words and Music by Daryl Hall

Suggested Registration: Jazz Organ
Rhythm: Soft Rock
Tempo: ♩ = 82

Babe, if we can't solve a-ny prob-lems, why do we lose_ so ma-ny

tears?_____ Oh,_ I saw you go a-gain,

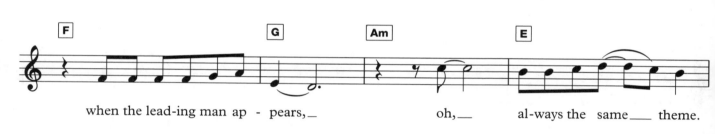

when the lead-ing man ap-pears,_ oh,_ al-ways the same_ theme.

Can't you see that we've got ev-ery-thing go-ing on and on_ and on,

and ev-ery-time you go a-way,_ you take a piece of

me with_ you, and ev-ery-time you go a-way,_

Eye Of The Tiger

Words and Music by Frank Sullivan and Jim Peterik

Suggested Registration: Distortion Guitar
Rhythm: Rock
Tempo: ♩ = 116

Ris-in' up __ back on the street __ did my time, took my

chan-ces, went the dis-tance, now I'm back on my feet, just a

man and his will to sur-vive. __ So ma-ny times it

hap-pens too fast, __ you trade your pas-sion for glo-ry,

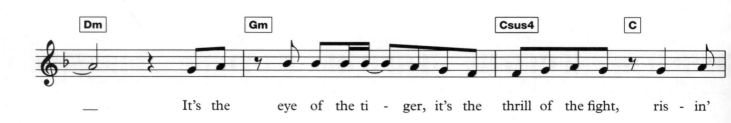

don't lose your grip on the dreams of the past, you must fight just to keep them a-live.

__ It's the eye of the ti-ger, it's the thrill of the fight, ris-in'

FAME

Words by Dean Pitchford / Music by Michael Gore

Suggested Registration: Saxophone
Rhythm: Rock
Tempo: ♩ = 124

Ba-by, look__ at me,__ and tell me what __ you see.__ You ain't seen__ the best__ of me yet, give me time,__ I'll make__ you for-get the rest. I got more __ in me,__ and you can set__ it free.__ I can catch__ the moon__ in my hand. Don't you know who I am?

GOLDEN BROWN

Words and Music by Hugh Cornwell, Jean Jacques Burnel, Jet Black and David Greenfield

Suggested Registration: Oboe
Rhythm: Jazz Waltz
Tempo: ♩ = 174

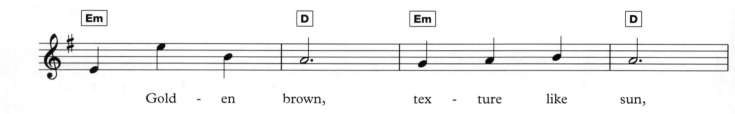

Gold - en brown, tex - ture like sun,

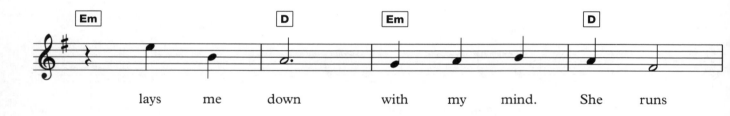

lays me down with my mind. She runs

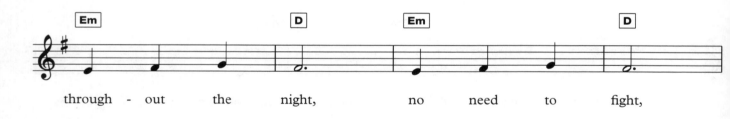

through - out the night, no need to fight,

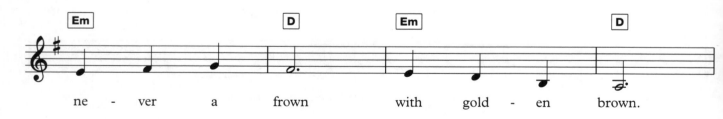

ne - ver a frown with gold - en brown.

Gold - en brown, fi - ner temp - tress,

through the age, she's head - ing west

from far a - way, stays for a day,

ne - ver a frown with gold - en brown.

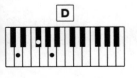

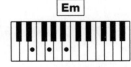

Happy Talk

Words by Oscar Hammerstein II / Music by Richard Rodgers

Suggested Registration: Clarinet
Rhythm: Swing
Tempo: ♩ = 190

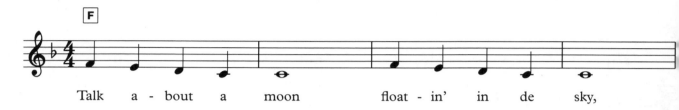

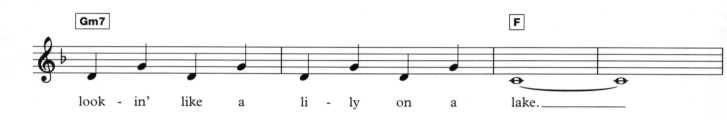

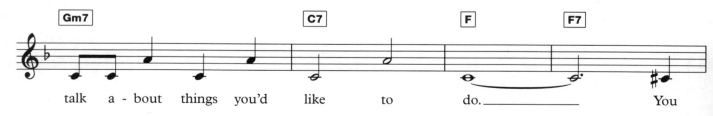

How Am I Supposed To Live Without You

Words and Music by Michael Bolton and Doug James

Suggested Registration: Electric Piano
Rhythm: Soft Rock
Tempo: ♩ = 68

I could hard-ly be-lieve it when I heard the news to-day, I

had to come and set it straight from you. ___ They said you were leav-ing, some-one's

swept your heart a-way. From the look up-on ___ your face, I see it's true. So

tell me all a-bout it, tell me 'bout the plans you're mak-ing, tell me one more thing be-fore I go.

Tell me, how am I ___ sup-posed to live with-out ___ you, ___

now that I've been lov-in' you ___ so long? ___

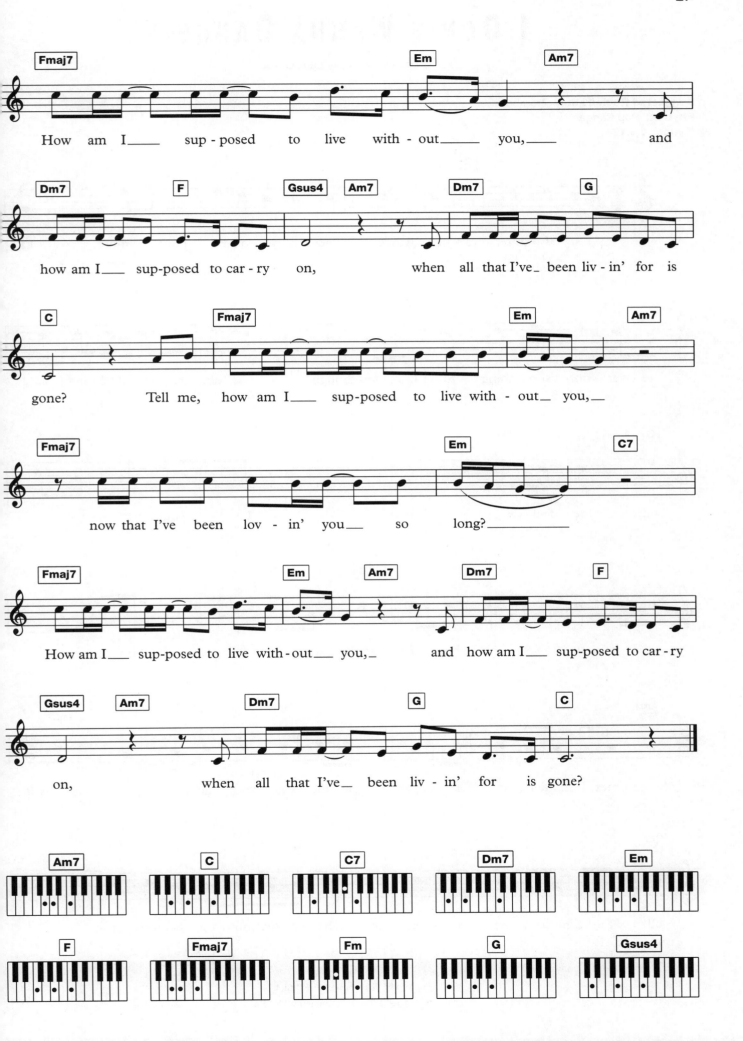

I Don't Wanna Dance

Words and Music by Eddy Grant

Suggested Registration: Trombone
Rhythm: Pop Reggae
Tempo: ♩ = 124

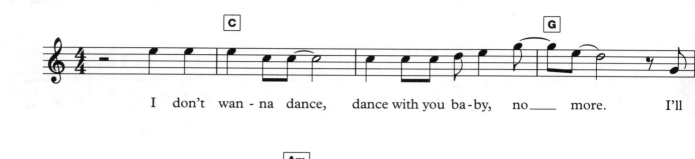

I don't wan-na dance, dance with you ba-by, no___ more. I'll

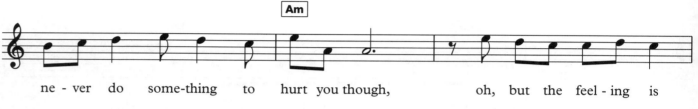

ne-ver do some-thing to hurt you though, oh, but the feel-ing is

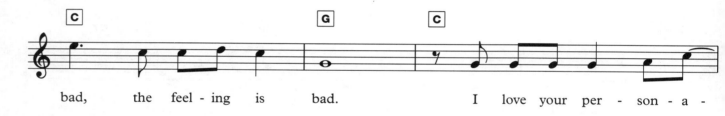

bad, the feel-ing is bad. I love your per-son-a-

-li-ty, oh, but I don't want our love on show.___

Some-times I think it's in-sa-ni-ty, girl, the way you go_____ with

all of the guys on the cor-ner. Oh ba-by, you're the la-test trick,___

oh, you seem to have their num - ber. Look they're danc - ing still, ___

___ but I don't wan - na dance, dance with you ba - by, no ___

___ more. ___ I'll ne - ver do some-thing to hurt you though,

oh, but the feel - ing is bad, the feel - ing is bad. I don't

wan - na dance, dance with you ba - by, no ___ more. ___ I'll

ne - ver do some-thing to hurt you though, oh, but the feel - ing is

bad, the feel - ing is bad. I don't wan - na dance.

I Want To Break Free

Words and Music by John Deacon

Suggested Registration: Electric Guitar
Rhythm: Rock Ballad / 8 Beat
Tempo: ♩ = 120

I want to break free, ___ I want to break free,

I want to break free from your lies, you're so self-sa-tis-fied, I don't

need ___ you. I've got to break free. God

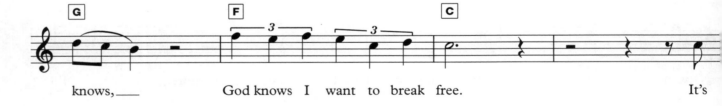

knows, ___ God knows I want to break free. It's

strange, but it's true, _____ hey, I can't get o-ver the way you

love me like you do, __ but I have to be sure when I walk out that door, __

oh how I want to be free, ba - by, oh how I want to be free,____

oh how I want to break free. But life still goes on._____

I can't get used to liv - ing with - out, liv - ing with - out,

liv - ing with - out you by my side._____

I don't want to live a - lone, God knows,____

God knows I want to break free._____

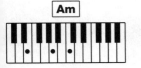
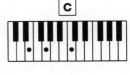
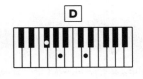
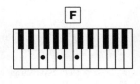
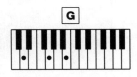

Karma Chameleon

Words and Music by George O'Dowd, Jon Moss, Michael Craig, Roy Hay and Phil Pickett

Suggested Registration: Harmonica
Rhythm: 8 Beat
Tempo: ♩ = 170

Des - ert lov - ing in___ your eyes all___ the way,

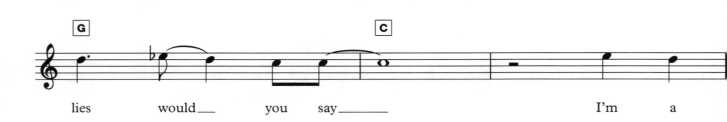

___ if I lis - ten___ to___ your

lies would___ you say_____ I'm a

man with - out___ con - vic - tion?___

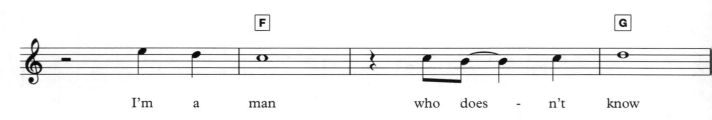

I'm a man who does - n't know

how to sell___ a con - tra - dic - tion.___

Land Of Make Believe

Words and Music by Andy Hill and Pete Sinfield

Suggested Registration: Synth Lead
Rhythm: 8 Beat / Pop
Tempo: ♩ = 172

Sha - dows

tap - ping at your win - dow, ghost -

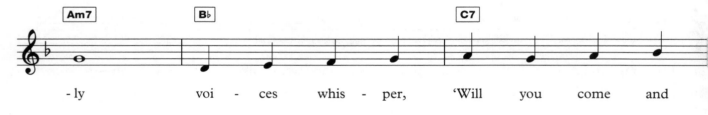

- ly voi - ces whis - per, 'Will you come and

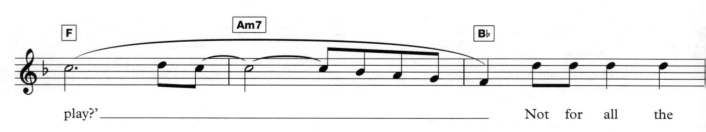

play?' _____ Not for all the

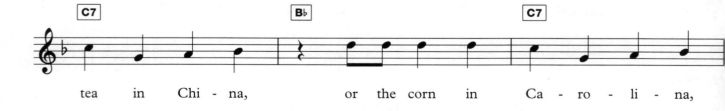

tea in Chi - na, or the corn in Ca - ro - li - na,

ne - ver,_____ ne - ver ev - er._____

— They're run - ning af - ter you____ babe.

Run for the sun____ lit - tle one, you're an

out - law once a - gain, time to change,__ Su - per -

- man will be with us while he can_____

— in the land of make be - lieve._____

LIKE A VIRGIN

Words and Music by Billy Steinberg and Tom Kelly

Suggested Registration: Organ
Rhythm: Soul
Tempo: ♩ = 124

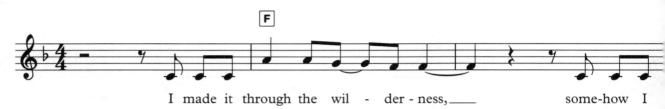

I made it through the wil - der - ness,____ some-how I

made it through,_____ did - n't know how

lost I was___ un - til I found you._____ I was beat,

___ in - com - plete,___ I'd been had,___ I was

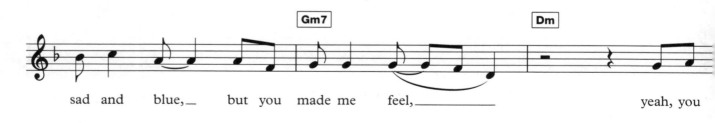

sad and blue,___ but you made me feel,_____ yeah, you

made_____ me feel____ shi - ny and new,___

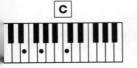 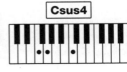 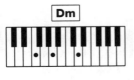 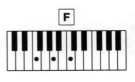 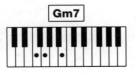

Love Is In The Air

Words and Music by Harry Vanda and George Young

Suggested Registration: Piano
Rhythm: Samba / Latin
Tempo: ♩ = 128

Love is in the air, ev - ery-where I look a - round,

love is in the air, ev - ery sight and ev - ery

sound, and I don't know if I'm be - ing

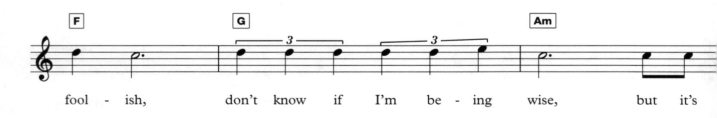

fool - ish, don't know if I'm be - ing wise, but it's

some-thing that I must be - lieve in, and it's there when I look in your

eyes.

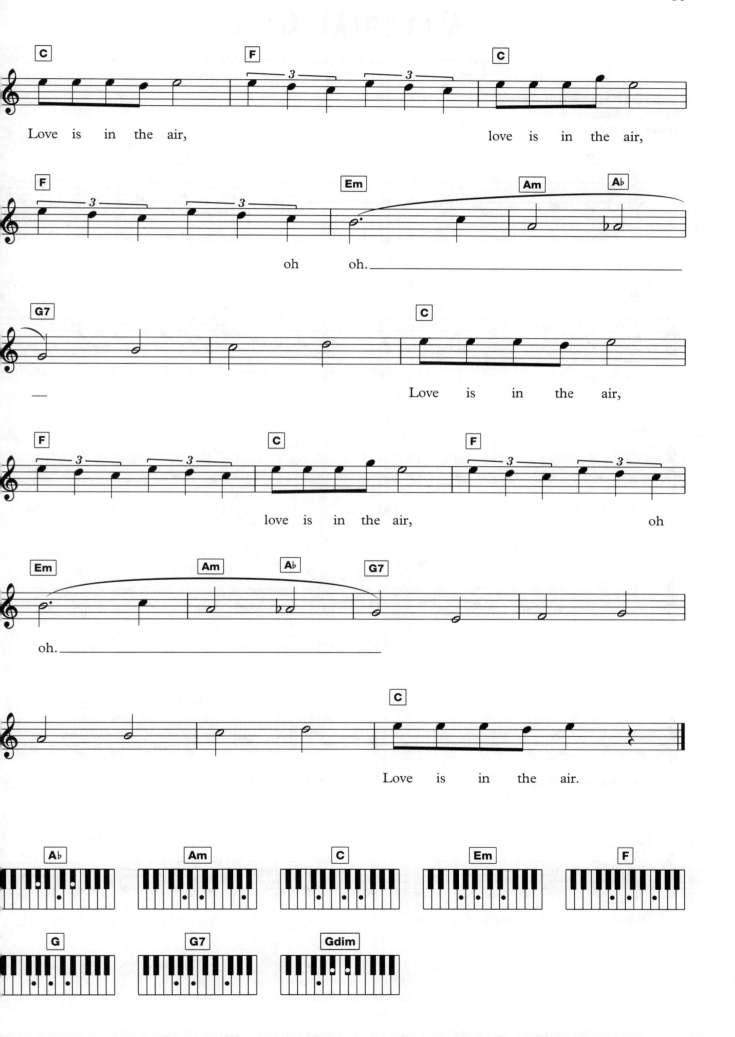

Material Girl

Words by Peter Brown and Robert Rans / Music by Peter Brown

Suggested Registration: Clarinet
Rhythm: 8 Beat
Tempo: ♩ = 136

Some boys kiss__ me, some boys hug__ me, I think they're O. K.

_____ if they don't give me pro - per cre - dit

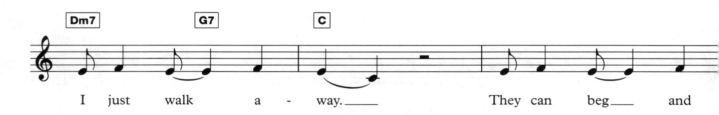

I just walk a - way.__ They can beg__ and

they can plead,_ but they can't see the light__ that's right,__

'cause the boy__ with the cold hard cash__ is al - ways Mis - ter

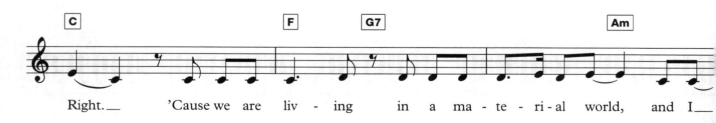

Right.__ 'Cause we are liv - ing in a ma - te - ri - al world, and I__

Nikita

Words by Bernie Taupin / Music by Elton John

Suggested Registration: Electric Piano
Rhythm: Soft Rock
Tempo: ♩ = 84

Hey Ni - ki - ta, is it cold in your lit - tle cor - ner of the world? You could roll a - round the globe,

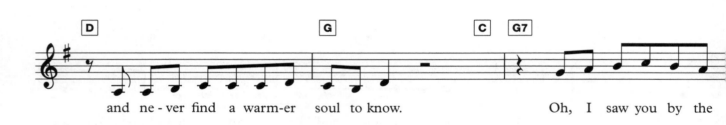

and ne - ver find a warm - er soul to know. Oh, I saw you by the

wall, ten of your tin sol - diers in a row,

with eyes that looked like ice on fire, the hu - man heart a cap - tive

in the snow. Oh Ni - ki - ta, you will ne - ver know

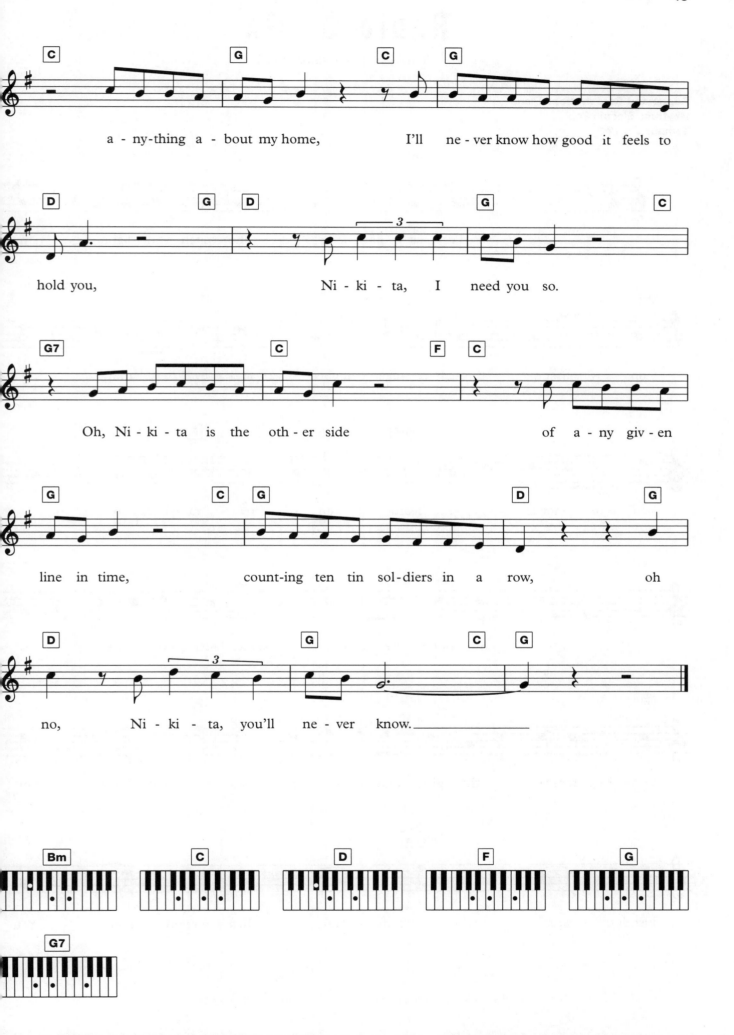

Radio Ga Ga

Words and Music by Roger Taylor

Suggested Registration: Piano
Rhythm: Electric Pop
Tempo: ♩ = 124

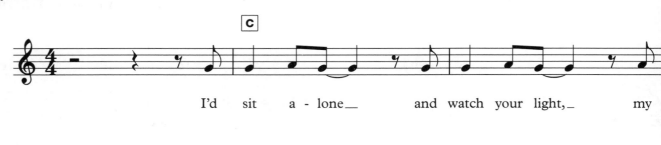

I'd sit a - lone___ and watch your light,___ my

on - ly friend through teen - age nights, and ev - ery - thing___ I

had to know,_ I heard it on___ my ra - di - o.___

So don't be - come___ some back - ground noise, a

back - drop for___ the girls and boys,_____ who just don't know, or

just don't care,_ and just com - plain___ when you're not there. You

Take My Breath Away

Words and Music by Giorgio Moroder and Tom Whitlock

Suggested Registration: Oboe
Rhythm: Ethnic / Soft Rock
Tempo: ♩ = 100

Watch-ing ev-ery mo-tion in____ my fool-ish lov-er's game,___

on this end-less o-cean fi - n'lly lov-ers know no shame,

turn-ing and re-turn-ing to___ some sec-ret place in - side._____

Watch-ing in slow mo - tion as___ you turn a-round and say,_____

'Take my breath a - way.'_____

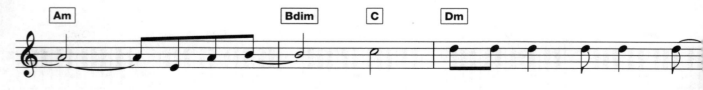

Through the hour-glass I saw_

47

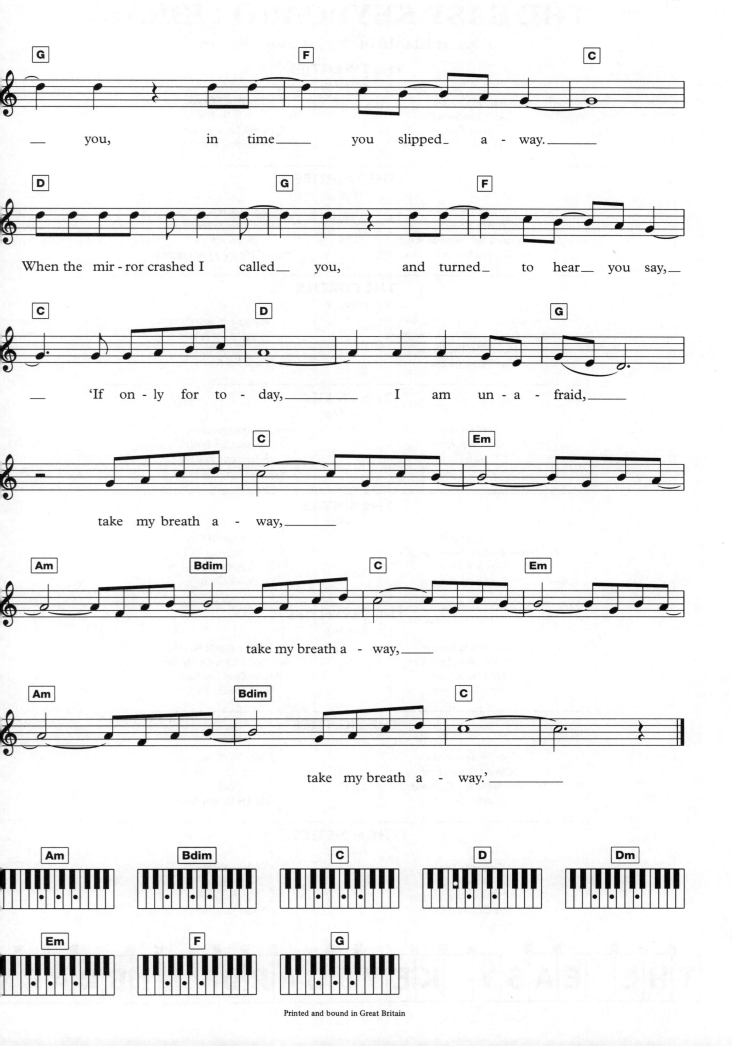

Printed and bound in Great Britain

THE EASY KEYBOARD LIBRARY

Also available in the Decades Series

THE TWENTIES
including:

Ain't Misbehavin'
Ain't She Sweet?
Baby Face
The Man I Love

My Blue Heaven
Side By Side
Spread A Little Happiness
When You're Smiling

THE THIRTIES
including:

All Of Me
A Fine Romance
I Wanna Be Loved By You
I've Got You Under My Skin

The Lady Is A Tramp
Smoke Gets In Your Eyes
Summertime
Walkin' My Baby Back Home

THE FORTIES
including:

Almost Like Being In Love
Don't Get Around Much Any More
How High The Moon
Let There Be Love

Sentimental Journey
Swinging On A Star
Tenderly
You Make Me Feel So Young

THE FIFTIES
including:

All The Way
Cry Me A River
Dream Lover
High Hopes

Magic Moments
Mister Sandman
A Teenager In Love
Whatever Will Be Will Be

THE SIXTIES
including:

Cabaret
Happy Birthday Sweet Sixteen
I'm A Believer
The Loco-motion

My Kind Of Girl
Needles And Pins
There's A Kind Of Hush
Walk On By

THE SEVENTIES
including:

Chanson D'Amour
Hi Ho Silver Lining
I'm Not In Love
Isn't She Lovely

Save Your Kisses For Me
Take Good Care Of My Baby
We've Only Just Begun
You Light Up My Life

THE EIGHTIES
including:

Anything For You
China In Your Hand
Everytime You Go Away
Golden Brown

I Want To Break Free
Karma Chameleon
Nikita
Take My Breath Away

THE NINETIES
including:

Crocodile Shoes
I Swear
A Million Love Songs
The One And Only

Promise Me
Sacrifice
Think Twice
Would I Lie To You?